CW00401901

YEAR 4

STAR MATHS STARTERS

A fresh approach to mental maths

TERMS AND CONDITIONS

IMPORTANT - PERMITTED USE AND WARNINGS - READ CAREFULLY BEFORE USING

Minimum specification:
- PC with a CD-ROM drive and 512 Mb RAM (recommended)
- Windows 98SE or above/Mac OSX.1 or above
- Recommended minimum processor speed: 1 GHz
- Facilities for printing

Julie Cogill and Anthony David

Authors
Julie Cogill and Anthony David

Anthony David dedicates this book to his wife Peachey, and sons Oliver and Samuel.

Editor
Niamh O'Carroll

Assistant Editor
Marion Archer

Illustrator
Theresa Tibbetts (Beehive Illustration)

Series Designer
Joy Monkhouse

Designers
Shelley Best and Melissa Leeke

Text © 2008 Julie Cogill and Anthony David
© 2008 Scholastic Ltd

CD-ROM development in association with Vivid Interactive

Designed using Adobe InDesign and Adobe Illustrator

Published by Scholastic Ltd
Villiers House, Clarendon Avenue,
Leamington Spa, Warwickshire CV32 5PR
www.scholastic.co.uk

Printed by Tien Wah, Singapore
1 2 3 4 5 6 7 8 9   8 9 0 1 2 3 4 5 6 7

ISBN 978-1407-10010-4

ACKNOWLEDGEMENTS
Extracts from the Primary National Strategy's *Primary Framework for Mathematics* (2006)
www.standards.dfes.gov.uk/primaryframework, *Renewing the Primary Framework* (2006) and the
Interactive Teaching Programs originally developed for the National Numeracy Strategy © Crown
copyright. Reproduced under the terms of the Click Use Licence.

Every effort has been made to trace copyright holders for the works reproduced in this book, and the
publishers apologise for any inadvertent omissions.

Introduction

In the 1999 *Framework for Teaching Mathematics* the first part of the daily mathematics lesson is described as 'whole-class work to rehearse, sharpen and develop mental and oral skills'. The Framework identified a number of short, focused activities that might form part of this oral and mental work. Teachers responded very positively to these 'starters' and they were often judged by Ofsted to be the strongest part of mathematics lessons.

However, the renewed *Primary Framework for Mathematics* (2006) highlights that the initial focus of 'starters', as rehearsing mental and oral skills, has expanded to become a vehicle for teaching a range of mathematics. 'Too often the "starter" has become an activity extended beyond the recommended five to ten minutes' (*Renewing the Primary Framework for mathematics: Guidance paper,* 2006). The renewed Framework also suggests that 'the focus on oral and mental calculation has been lost and needs to be reinvigorated'.

Star Maths Starters aims to 'freshen up' the oral and mental starter by providing focused activities that help to secure children's knowledge and sharpen their oral and mental skills. It is a new series, designed to provide classes and teachers with a bank of stimulating interactive whiteboard resources for use as starter activities. Each of the 30 starters offers a short, focused activity designed for the first five to ten minutes of the daily mathematics lesson. Equally, the starters can be used as stand-alone oral and mental maths 'games' to get the most from a spare ten minutes in the day.

About the book

Each book includes a bank of teachers' notes linked to the interactive whole-class activities on the CD-ROM. A range of additional support is also provided, including planning grids, classroom resources, generic support for using the interactive whiteboard in mathematics lessons, and an objectives grid.

Objectives grid
A comprehensive two-page planning grid identifies links to the *Primary Framework for Mathematics* strands and objectives. The grid also identifies one of six starter types, appropriate to each interactive activity (see page 7 for further information).

Starter Number	Star Starter Title	Page No.	Strand	Learning objective as taken from the Primary Framework for Mathematics	Type of Starter
16	Fractions (ITP)	28	Knowing and using number facts	Identify pairs of fractions that total 1	Refresh
17	Maths Boggle: addition and subtraction	29	Calculating	Add or subtract mentally pairs of two-digit whole numbers	Refine
18	Function machine	30	Calculating	Add or subtract mentally pairs of two-digit whole numbers	Reason
19	Shopping	31	Calculating	Refine and use efficient written methods to add £.p	Refine
20	Bingo: times tables (×10 and ×100)	32	Calculating	Multiply numbers to 1000 by 10 and then 100 (whole-number answers)	Refine
21	Finding reflections	33	Understanding shape	Draw polygons and identify their properties, including their line symmetry	Refine
22	Maps and directions	34	Understanding shape	Use the eight compass points to describe direction	Rehearse
23	Find the alien: coordinates	35	Understanding shape	Describe and identify the position of a point on a grid of squares	Reason
24	Calculating angles (ITP)	36	Understanding shape	Know that angles are measured in degrees and that one turn is 360°; compare and order angles less than 180°	Reason

Highlighted text indicates the end-of-year objectives

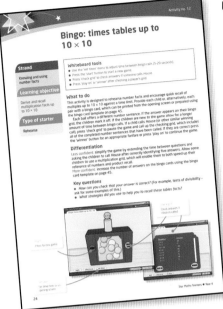

Activity pages

Each page of teachers' notes includes:

Learning objectives
Covering the strands and objectives of the renewed *Primary Framework for Mathematics*

Type of starter
Identifying one or more of the 'six Rs' of oral and mental work (see page 7)

Whiteboard tools
Identifying the key functions of the accompanying CD-ROM activity

What to do
Outline notes on how to administer the activity with the whole class

Differentiation
Adapting the activity for more or less confident learners

Key questions
Probing questions to stimulate and sustain the oral and mental work

Annotations
At-a-glance instructions for using the CD-ROM activity.

Whiteboard hints and tips

Each title offers some general support identifying practical mathematical activities that can be performed on any interactive whiteboard (see pages 8–9).

Recording sheets

Two recording sheets have been included to support your planning:
- Planning for the six Rs: plan a balance of activities across the six Rs of mental and oral maths (see page 7).
- Star Maths Starters diary: build a record of the starters used (titles, objectives covered, how they were used and dates they were used).

About the CD-ROM

Types of activity

Each CD-ROM contains 30 interactive starter activities for use on any interactive whiteboard. These include:

Interactive whiteboard resources
A set of engaging interactive activities specifically designed for *Star Maths Starters*. The teachers' notes on pages 13–42 of this book explain how each activity can be used for a ten-minute mental maths starter, with annotated screen shots giving you at-a-glance support. Similarly, a 'what to do' function within each activity provides at-the-board support.

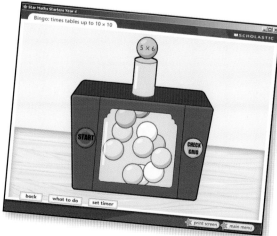

Interactive teaching programs (ITPs)

A small number of ITPs, originally developed by the National Numeracy Strategy, has been included on each CD-ROM. They are simple programs that model a range of objectives, such as data presentation or place value. Their strength is that they are easy to read and use. If you press the Esc button the ITP will reduce to a window on the computer screen. It can then be enlarged or more ITPs can be launched and set up to model further objectives, or simply to extend the objective from that starter. To view the relevant 'what to do' notes once an ITP is open, press the Esc button to gain access to the function on the opening screen of the activity.

Interactive 'notepad'

A pop-up 'notepad' is built into a variety of activities. This allows the user to write answers or keep a record of workings out and includes 'pen', 'eraser' and 'clear' tools.

Teacher zone

This teachers' section includes links from the interactive activities to the *Primary Framework for Mathematics* strands, together with editable objectives grids, planning grids and printable versions of the activity sheets on pages 43–46.

How to use the CD-ROM

System requirements

Minimum specification
● PC with a CD-ROM drive and 512 Mb RAM (recommended)
● Windows 98SE or above/Mac OSX.1 or above
● Recommended minimum processor speed: 1 GHz

Getting started

The *Star Maths Starters* CD-ROM should auto run when inserted into your CD drive. If it does not, use **My Computer** to browse the contents of the CD-ROM and click on the 'Star Maths Starters' icon.

From the start-up screen you will find four options: select **Credits** to view a list of credits. Click on **Register** to register the product to receive product updates and special offers. Click on **How to use** to access support notes for using the CD-ROM. Finally, if you agree to the terms and conditions, select **Start** to move to the main menu.

For all technical support queries, please phone Scholastic Customer Services on 0845 6039091.

The six Rs of oral and mental work

In the guidance paper *Renewing the Primary Framework for mathematics* (2006), the Primary National Strategy identified six features of children's mathematical learning that oral and mental work can support. The description of the learning and an outline of possible activities are given below:

Six Rs	Learning focus	Possible activities
Rehearse	To practise and consolidate existing skills, usually mental calculation skills, set in a context to involve children in problem solving through the use and application of these skills; use of vocabulary and language of number, properties of shapes or describing and reasoning.	Interpret words such as more, less, sum, altogether, difference, subtract; find missing numbers or missing angles on a straight line; say the number of days in four weeks or the number of 5p coins that make up 35p; describe part-revealed shapes, hidden solids; describe patterns or relationships; explain decisions or why something meets criteria.
Recall	To secure knowledge of facts, usually number facts; build up speed and accuracy; recall quickly names and properties of shapes, units of measure or types of charts, graphs to represent data.	Count on and back in steps of constant size; recite the 6-times table and derive associated division facts; name a shape with five sides or a solid with five flat faces; list properties of cuboids; state units of time and their relationships.
Refresh	To draw on and revisit previous learning; to assess, review and strengthen children's previously acquired knowledge and skills relevant to later learning; return to aspects of mathematics with which the children have had difficulty; draw out key points from learning.	Refresh multiplication facts or properties of shapes and associated vocabulary; find factor pairs for given multiples; return to earlier work on identifying fractional parts of given shapes; locate shapes in a grid as preparation for lessons on coordinates; refer to general cases and identify new cases.
Refine	To sharpen methods and procedures; explain strategies and solutions; extend ideas and develop and deepen the children's knowledge; reinforce their understanding of key concepts; build on earlier learning so that strategies and techniques become more efficient and precise.	Find differences between two two-digit numbers, extend to three-digit numbers to develop skill; find 10% of quantities, then 5% and 20% by halving and doubling; use audible and quiet counting techniques to extend skills; give coordinates of shapes in different orientations to hone concept; review informal calculation strategies.
Read	To use mathematical vocabulary and interpret images, diagrams and symbols correctly; read number sentences and provide equivalents; describe and explain diagrams and features involving scales, tables or graphs; identify shapes from a list of their properties; read and interpret word problems and puzzles; create their own problems and lines of enquiry.	Tell a story using an interactive bar chart; alter the chart for children to retell the story; starting with a number sentence (eg 2 + 11 = 13), children generate and read equivalent statements for 13; read values on scales with different intervals; read information about a shape and eliminate possible shapes; set number sentences in given contexts; read others' results and offer new questions and ideas for enquiry.
Reason	To use and apply acquired knowledge, skills and understanding; make informed choices and decisions, predict and hypothesise; use deductive reasoning to eliminate or conclude; provide examples that satisfy a condition always, sometimes or never and say why.	Sort shapes into groups and give reasons for selection; discuss why alternative methods of calculation work and when to use them; decide what calculation to do in a problem and explain the choice; deduce a solid from a 2D picture; use fractions to express proportions; draw conclusions from given statements to solve puzzles.

Each one of the styles of starter enables children to access different mathematical skills and each has a different outcome, as identified above. A bingo game, for example, provides a good way of rehearsing number facts, whereas a 'scales' activity supports reading skills. In the objectives grid on pages 10–11, the type of each Star Starters activity is identified to make it easier to choose appropriate styles of starter matched to a particular objective. A 'Six Rs' recording sheet has also been provided on page 12 (with an editable version on the CD-ROM) to track the types of starter you will be using against the strands of the renewed Framework.

Using the interactive whiteboard in primary mathematics

The interactive whiteboard is an invaluable tool for teaching and learning mathematics. It can be used to demonstrate and model mathematical concepts to the whole class, offering the potential to share children's learning experiences. It gives access to powerful resources - audio, video, images, websites and interactive activities - to discuss, interact with and learn from. *Star Maths Starters* provides 30 quality interactive resources that are easy to set up and use and which help children to improve their mathematical development and thinking skills through their use as short, focused oral and mental starters.

Whiteboard resources and children's learning

There are many reasons why the whiteboard, especially in mathematics, enhances children's learning:

- Using high-quality interactive maths resources will engage children in the process of learning and developing their mathematical thinking skills. Resources such as maths games can create a real sense of theatre in the whole class and promote a real desire to achieve and succeed in a task.
- As mentioned above, the whiteboard can be used to demonstrate some very important mathematical concepts. For example, many teachers find that children understand place value much faster and more thoroughly through using interactive resources on a whiteboard. Similarly, the whiteboard can support children's visualisation of mathematics, especially for 'Shape and Space' activities.
- Although mathematics usually has a correct or incorrect answer, there are often several ways of reaching the same result. The whiteboard allows the teacher to demonstrate methods and encourages children to present and compare their own mental or written methods of calculation.

Using a whiteboard in Year 4

An interactive whiteboard can be used for a variety of purposes in Year 4 mathematics lessons. These include:

- helping children to visualise number patterns using interactive number squares or number lines;
- demonstrating decimal notation for tenths and hundredths and how to partition decimals;
- using diagrams to identify equivalent fractions; highlighting the position of fractions or decimals on a number line;
- using software programs to help visualise 3D objects - for example, nets of shapes can be constructed and deconstructed at the touch of a button;
- using software to teach the 'data-handling cycle': start with a question, collect data, process and present the data on the whiteboard, ask the whole class to interpret the data and answer questions about it.

Practical considerations

For the teacher, the whiteboard has the potential to save preparation and classroom time, as well as providing more flexible teaching.

ICT resources for the interactive whiteboard often involve numbers that are randomly generated, so that possible questions or calculations stemming from a single resource may be many and varied. This enables resources to be used for a longer or shorter time period depending on the purpose of the activity and how children's learning is progressing. *Star Maths Starters* includes many activities of this type.

From the very practical point of view of saving teachers' time, particularly in the starter activity, it is often easier to set up mathematics resources more quickly than those for other subjects. Once the software is familiar, preparation time is saved especially when there is need for clear presentation, as in drawing shapes accurately or creating charts and diagrams for 'Handling data' activities.

Maths resources on the interactive whiteboard are often flexible and enable differentiation so that a teacher can access different degrees of difficulty using the same software. Last but not least, whiteboard resources save time writing on the board and software often checks calculations, if required, which enables more time both for teaching and assessing children's understanding.

Using *Star Maths Starters* interactively

Much has been said and written about interactivity in the classroom but it is not always clear what this means. For example, children coming out to the board and ticking a box is not what is meant by 'whole-class interactive teaching and learning'. In mathematics it is about challenging children's ideas so that they develop their own thinking skills and, when appropriate, encouraging them to make connections across different mathematical topics. As a teacher, this means asking suitable questions and encouraging children to explore and discuss their methods of calculation and whether there are alternative ways of achieving the same result. *Star Maths Starters* provides some examples of key questions that could be asked while the activities are being undertaken, together with suggestions for how to engage less confident learners and stretch the more confident.

If you already have some experience in using the whiteboard interactively then we hope the teaching suggestions set out in this book will take you further. What is especially important is the facility the whiteboard provides to share pupils' mathematical learning experiences. This does not mean just asking children to suggest answers, but using the facility of the board to display and discuss ideas so that everyone can share in the learning experience. Obviously, this needs to be in a way that explores and relates the thinking of individuals to the context of the learning that is happening.

In the best whiteboard classrooms, teachers comment that the board provides a shared learning experience between the teacher and the class, in so far as the teacher may sometimes stand aside while children themselves are discussing their own mathematical methods and ideas.

Starter Number	Star Starter Title	Page No.	Strand	Learning objective as taken from the Primary Framework for Mathematics	Type of Starter
1	Find the missing number	13	Using and applying mathematics	Represent a puzzle using number sentences and use these to solve a problem	Reason
2	Prediction using number squares	14	Counting and understanding number	Recognise and continue number sequences formed by counting on or back in steps of constant size	Refresh
3	Pirates: multiples of 10 and 100	15	Counting and understanding number	Recognise and continue number sequences formed by counting on or back in steps of constant size	Recall
4	Twenty cards (ITP): largest and smallest numbers	16	Counting and understanding number	Partition, round and order four-digit whole numbers	Reason
5	Decimals on the number line	17	Counting and understanding number	Use decimal notation for tenths	Refine
6	Bricks: ordering decimals	18	Counting and understanding number	Position one-place decimals	Reason
7	Sorting machine: decimals and fractions	19	Counting and understanding number	Recognise the equivalence between decimal and fraction forms of one half, quarters, tenths and hundredths	Refresh
8	Finding patterns and proportions	20	Counting and understanding number	Use the vocabulary of ratio and proportion to describe the relationship between two quantities	Read
9	Targets: number facts	21	Knowing and using number facts	Use knowledge of addition and subtraction facts to derive sums of numbers (up to the tenth multiple)	Rehearse
10	Place value (ITP)	22	Knowing and using number facts	Use knowledge of addition and subtraction facts and place value to derive sums and differences of pairs of multiples of 10, 100 or 1000	Refine
11	Multiplication square	23	Knowing and using number facts	Derive and recall multiplication facts up to 10×10	Rehearse
12	Bingo: times tables up to 10×10	24	Knowing and using number facts	Derive and recall multiplication facts up to 10×10	Rehearse
13	Dominoes: multiplication	25	Knowing and using number facts	Derive and recall multiplication facts up to 10×10	Rehearse
14	Number dials (ITP)	26	Knowing and using number facts	Derive and recall multiplication facts up to 10×10, the corresponding division facts and multiples of numbers to 10 up to the tenth multiple	Refine
15	Dominoes: fractions that total 1	27	Knowing and using number facts	Identify pairs of fractions that total 1	Reason

Starter Number	Star Starter Title	Page No.	Strand	Learning objective as taken from the Primary Framework for Mathematics	Type of Starter
16	Fractions (ITP)	28	Knowing and using number facts	Identify pairs of fractions that total 1	Refresh
17	Maths Boggle: addition and subtraction	29	Calculating	Add or subtract mentally pairs of two-digit whole numbers	Refine
18	Function machine	30	Calculating	Add or subtract mentally pairs of two-digit whole numbers	Reason
19	Shopping	31	Calculating	Refine and use efficient written methods to add £.p	Refine
20	Bingo: times tables (×10 and ×100)	32	Calculating	Multiply numbers to 1000 by 10 and then 100 (whole-number answers)	Refine
21	Finding reflections	33	Understanding shape	Draw polygons and identify their properties, including their line symmetry	Refine
22	Maps and directions	34	Understanding shape	Use the eight compass points to describe direction	Rehearse
23	Find the alien: coordinates	35	Understanding shape	Describe and identify the position of a point on a grid of squares	Reason
24	Calculating angles (ITP)	36	Understanding shape	Know that angles are measured in degrees and that one turn is 360°; compare and order angles less than 180°	Reason
25	Maths Boggle: measurements	37	Measuring	Choose and use standard metric units and their abbreviations when estimating, measuring and recording and, where appropriate, use decimal notation to record measurements	Refine
26	Weighing scales	38	Measuring	Know the meaning of 'kilo' and, where appropriate, use decimal notation to record measurements	Read
27	Measuring jug	39	Measuring	Interpret intervals and divisions on partially numbered scales and record readings accurately	Refine
28	Finding area and perimeter	40	Measuring	Draw rectangles and measure and calculate their perimeters; find the area of rectilinear shapes drawn on a square grid by counting squares	Refine
29	Clocks: time differences	41	Measuring	Read time to the nearest minute; calculate time intervals from clocks	Read
30	Favourite colours	42	Handling data	Present, analyse and interpret data in bar charts using ICT	Refine

Planning for the six Rs of oral and mental work

Oral and mental activity – six Rs	Using and applying mathematics	Counting and understanding number	Knowing and using number facts	Calculating	Understanding shape	Measuring	Handling data
Rehearse			• Targets: number facts • Multiplication square • Bingo: times tables up to 10 × 10 • Dominoes: multiplication		• Maps and directions		
Recall		• Pirates: multiples of 10 and 100					
Refresh		• Prediction using number squares • Sorting machine: decimals and fractions	• Fractions (ITP)				
Refine		• Decimals on the number line	• Place value (ITP) • Number dials (ITP)	• Maths Boggle: addition and subtraction • Shopping • Bingo: times tables (×10 and ×100)	• Finding reflections	• Maths Boggle: measurements • Measuring jug • Finding area and perimeter	• Favourite colours
Read	• Find the missing number	• Finding patterns and proportions				• Weighing scales • Clocks: time differences	
Reason		• Twenty cards (ITP): largest and smallest numbers • Bricks: ordering decimals	• Dominoes: fractions that total 1	• Function machine	• Find the alien: coordinates • Calculating angles (ITP)		

Find the missing number

Strand

Using and applying mathematics

Learning objective

Represent a puzzle using number sentences; use these to solve a problem

Type of starter

Reason

Whiteboard tools
● Move cards and symbols onto the line to build a number sentence.
● Drag and drop numbers and symbols within a line to re-order them.
● Drag cards off the line to remove them.
● Press 'reset' to start again.

What to do
The aim of the activity is to find the missing number or numbers in a number sentence so that both sides of the equals sign (=) balance, using addition and subtraction methods. Numbers of any size can be selected as two digits selected consecutively snap together to form a two-digit number, three digits form a three-digit number and so on. For Year 4 use numbers up to 100 in order to tease out the logic and understanding of how to find the missing number rather than asking the children to complete complex calculations. Try to prepare number sentences that have more than one possible solution. For example: in solving $3 + \triangle + \square = 20$, $\triangle$ and $\square$ could be any numbers that add up to 17.

Differentiation
Less confident: start with simple straightforward sentences such as $3 + 10 = \square$ until children get used to the idea that the symbol represents a number.
More confident: ask children to make up their own number sentences to challenge the whole class. They may quickly learn that it is not always quite as easy as it looks as more than one solution is often possible.

Key questions
● *What is the missing number (or numbers), and are there any other numbers that might work?*
● *Are there any number sentences using addition and subtraction that don't always work?*

number sentence
Drag numbers and symbols to re-order

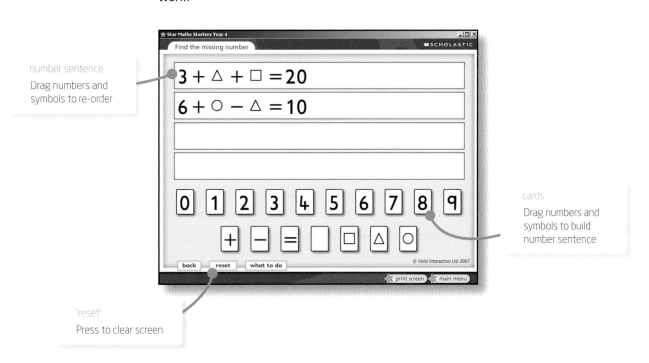

cards
Drag numbers and symbols to build number sentence

'reset'
Press to clear screen

Prediction using number squares

Strand

Counting and understanding number

Learning objective

Recognise and continue number sequences formed by counting on or back in steps of constant size

Type of starter

Refresh

Whiteboard tools

● Select one of the following number squares using the 'options' menu:
  1 to 100 stepping in 1s - select squares 10; start no. 1; step 1
  2 to 200 stepping in 2s - select squares 10; start no. 2; steps 2
  5 to 500 stepping in 5s - select squares 10; start no. 5; steps 5
  10 to 1000 stepping in 10s - select squares 10; start no. 10; steps 10.
● Press the 'highlight' or 'clear' button and then select any square to reveal the number beneath.

What to do

Prepare the number square before the session. Press the 'clear' button and reveal four or five numbers on the grid by clicking on them. Challenge the children to find all the remaining hidden numbers on the square. The key to this activity is in the selection of questions as this will draw out the children's understanding of number (see 'Key questions'). After each selection, press on the square to confirm or refute the children's prediction. Ask for more than one prediction before revealing the missing number.

Differentiation

Less confident: start the activity using the 1-100 square and stepping in ones until the children become familiar with the activity.
More confident: move on to squares using larger numbers and different step sizes (see 'Whiteboard tools').

Key questions

● *What are the numbers above and below the number showing?*
● *What are the numbers to the left and right of the number showing?*
● *What numbers are across the diagonals from the number showing?*
● *Who can predict the numbers in a whole row or column?*

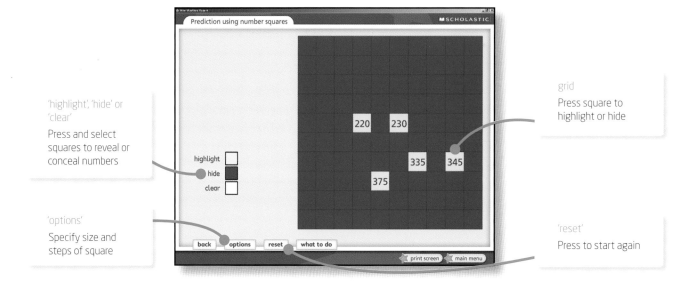

'highlight', 'hide' or 'clear'
Press and select squares to reveal or conceal numbers

'options'
Specify size and steps of square

grid
Press square to highlight or hide

'reset'
Press to start again

Pirates: multiples of 10 and 100

Strand

Counting and understanding number

Learning objective

Recognise and continue number sequences formed by counting on or back in steps of constant size

Type of starter

Recall

Whiteboard tools

- Start point: the pirate starts at the bottom of the mast or zero.
- Move the pirate up and down the mast in steps of 100 to answer a maths problem or number sentence.
- Select options for moving up and down (select from 'up only' or 'up and down'), and whether to show or hide the number sentence.
- Press 'new' to move the pirate back to the starting point and to generate a new question.
- Use the 'notepad' to show calculations.
- Press 'answer' to reveal the answer.

What to do

Use this activity to encourage children to add or subtract mentally in steps of 100. Ask them to use their individual whiteboards so that they can work out the answers for themselves prior to any class discussion. Extend the activity beyond the initial question by asking, for example: *What would happen if the pirate now moves down 200 steps?* Illustrate this by dragging and dropping the pirate to the new position. If required, set options for questions involving counting on ('up') before moving on to both types of question ('up and down'). Also, vary the base number in subsequent sessions so that the pirate always starts at 90, for example.

Differentiation

Less confident: support children with the photocopiable 'Pirates' sheet on page 43 and setting some questions with the pirate always starting at zero until the children have understood what is required.

More confident: ask children what they think would happen if the pirate moves down below zero.

Key questions

- *On which number does the pirate end up? How do you know?*
- *How far up or down the mast would the pirate need to climb to reach, for example, the 500 mark?*

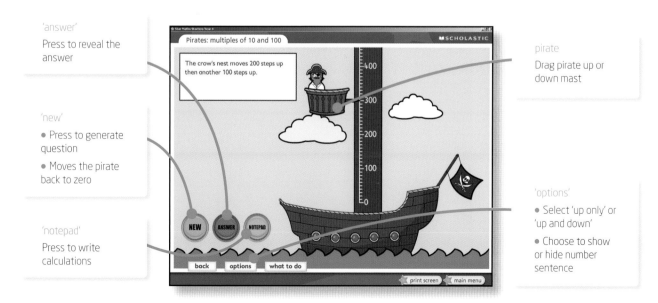

'answer'
Press to reveal the answer

'new'
- Press to generate question
- Moves the pirate back to zero

'notepad'
Press to write calculations

pirate
Drag pirate up or down mast

'options'
- Select 'up only' or 'up and down'
- Choose to show or hide number sentence

The crow's nest moves 200 steps up then another 100 steps up.

Twenty cards (ITP): largest and smallest numbers

Strand

Counting and understanding number

Learning objective

Partition, round and order four-digit whole numbers

Type of starter

Reason

Whiteboard tools
- Press the pack of cards with the blue outline and select 'random numbers' from the menu.
- Move the arrow to the right of 'How many cards' to 4.
- Move the arrow to the right of 'Maximum number' to 9.
- Leave 'Minimum number' at zero.
- Press 'go'.
- Four cards will be stacked up which can be dragged and dropped into the middle of the screen.
- Press the red part of a card to reveal each number.
- Drag the cards by their centres to re-arrange them in order.

What to do

Tell the children that the aim of this activity is to make the largest and smallest numbers possible using four cards. Spread the four cards out in a line and press the red part of each card to reveal each digit in turn. Ask the children to write the largest numbers possible using these four numbers on their individual whiteboards. Re-arrange the cards on the board and question the children about why they decided on a particular arrangement of the cards. Prompt for understanding using language such as *the thousands place; the hundreds place* and so on.

Differentiation

Less confident: ask the children to make the largest and smallest number using just three cards.
More confident: try using five or more cards, extending children's vocabulary to the language of larger numbers.

Key questions
- *What is the largest and smallest number that can be made with these four cards?*
- *How do you know that this is the largest number that can be made?*

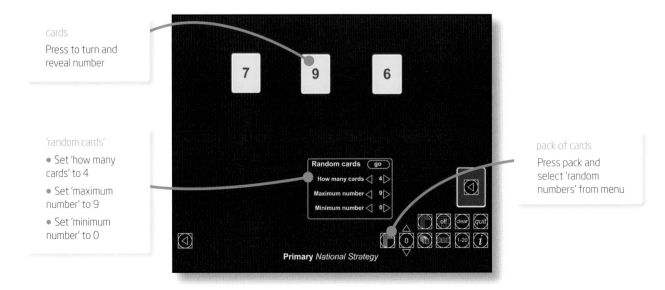

cards
Press to turn and reveal number

'random cards'
- Set 'how many cards' to 4
- Set 'maximum number' to 9
- Set 'minimum number' to 0

pack of cards
Press pack and select 'random numbers' from menu

Decimals on the number line

Strand

Counting and understanding number

Learning objective

Use decimal notation for tenths

Type of starter

Refine

Whiteboard tools

● Drag the red marker across the number line to position it.
● Drag the green marker across the number line to position it.
● Hide the values of the red and green marker numbers using the 'options' button.
● Start at a different whole number between 1 and 9 using the 'options' button.

What to do

Move the red marker to a decimal number and ask the children to read the number. Then ask them to count up in ones from the starting point. In a similar way drag the green marker to a decimal number and ask children to count down in ones from the number on the green marker. The 'options' button allows you to vary the start and end numbers on the number line and to show or hide the numbers on the markers. Vary these options during the session to give the children a greater appreciation of the value and position of decimal numbers on the number line.

Differentiation

Less confident: use the most basic number line from 0 to 10. Also, move the markers to whole numbers at first until they are more confident.
More confident: use different starting point numbers; or drag and drop both pointers and ask children to find the difference between the two numbers.

Key questions

● *What would the new number be if 0, 1 or 2... is added to the red marker number?*
● *What would the new number be if 0, 1, or 2... is subtracted from the green marker number?*

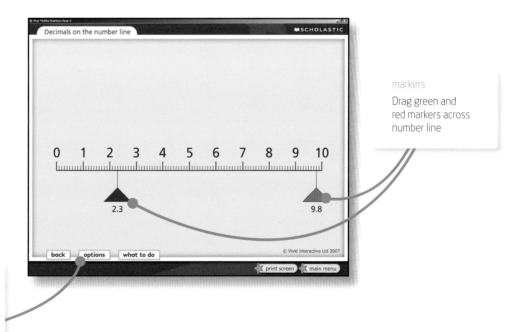

markers
Drag green and red markers across number line

'options'
● Select start number between 1 and 9
● Hide marker values
● Select 10 subdivisions

Bricks: ordering decimals

Strand

Counting and understanding number

Learning objective

Position one-place decimals

Type of starter

Reason

Whiteboard tools

● Use the option to fix the first digit of the numbers, if required.
● Press 'go' to generate five bricks, each showing a number between 0 and 10 with one decimal place.
● Drag each brick into the gaps in the wall, with the smallest number in the lowest position, to complete the wall.
● If five bricks are positioned correctly, a 'Well done' message appears. If any bricks are placed incorrectly, a 'Try again' message appears. Press 'ok' and the bricks move back to their starting position.
● Press 'go' again to select a new set of bricks.

What to do

Use this activity either to rehearse existing strategies for ordering decimals or to probe children's reasoning. Press 'go' to reveal five bricks, each showing a number between 0 and 10 with one decimal place. Ask the children to work as a whole class to decide the correct order, in pairs by writing answers on their individual whiteboards, or individually. Position the bricks in the wall by dragging and dropping them, or ask individual children to place them.

Differentiation

Less confident: use a number line to support the children's ordering skills before positioning the bricks in the wall. Fix the first digit to limit the number range.
More confident: ask the children what would need to be added to the top brick to make 10.

Key questions

● *What does the number to the right/left of the decimal point represent on each brick?*
● *What would the new number be if 1, 2 or 3… is added to the number on the lowest brick?*

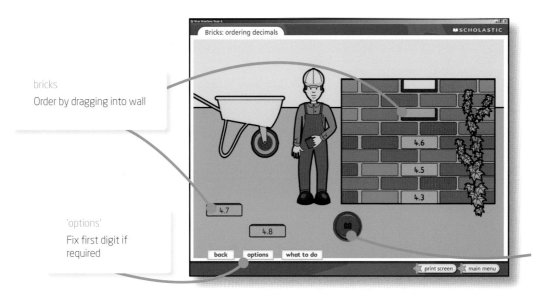

bricks
Order by dragging into wall

'options'
Fix first digit if required

'go'
Press to generate new bricks

Sorting machine: decimals and fractions

Strand

Counting and understanding number

Learning objective

Recognise the equivalence between decimal and fraction forms of one half, quarters, tenths and hundredths

Type of starter

Refresh

Whiteboard tools
- Press 'go' to launch the decimals and fractions individually into the machine.
- Press the cogs to select which bucket the decimal or fraction should go into.
- Press 'reset' to clear the machine and generate new decimals and fractions.

What to do

The aim of this starter is to sort equivalent decimals and fractions into the appropriate 'buckets'. For each fraction produced by the computer the children will have to decide whether it firstly is less or greater than 0.5 and then, secondly, whether it is either less or greater than 0.3. Use this activity to develop reasoning skills by encouraging children to predict their answers, explain their reasoning and then apply a test using the sorting machine. Children should also be encouraged to use the appropriate maths language at all times. When the children have completed the activity, check that they have sorted the decimals correctly. Discuss any misconceptions.

Differentiation

Less confident: provide a fraction chart to support less confident learners.
More confident: encourage the children to predict which bucket the number should go into when it first appears before going through the sorting system. Ask them to focus on sorting the fifths (one-fifth, two-fifths and three-fifths).

Key questions
- *What part of the number are we investigating in order to accurately sort it?*
- *What other fractions can you think of? How would they be sorted?*

'go'
Press to launch fraction

cogs
Use to sort fractions

'reset'
Press to start again

Finding patterns and proportions

Strand

Counting and understanding number

Learning objective

Use the vocabulary of ratio and proportion to describe the relationship between two quantities

Type of starter

Read

Whiteboard tools

- Select the number of beads required from the 'options' menu. Choose a length of 18 beads, 20 beads or 24 beads.
- Choose different colours from the palette and build up a pattern.
- If a colour needs to be removed, select the white colour and then press the appropriate bead.
- Press 'clear' to start again.

What to do

Create a pattern of beads using two or three colours. Note that to fit the bead length chosen, the number of beads used in the pattern must divide into the bead length used with no remainder. So, for example, if the length of beads chosen is 18 the pattern should use two, three, six or nine beads. Ask the children to predict the pattern themselves and continue the pattern using squared paper. Once the pattern has been established, encourage the children to use the correct vocabulary to describe proportions (for example: *two out of every three beads are blue*).

Differentiation

Less confident: use two colours only so that children get used to using the correct language and concentrate on their predictions in the early stages of the activity rather than use of language.

More confident: use three colours and extend the children's vocabulary to expressing the proportions of fractions (for example: *two fifths of the squares are red*).

Key questions

- *What do you think are the next ten beds in the pattern?*
- *How would you describe the number of different coloured beads in the pattern?*

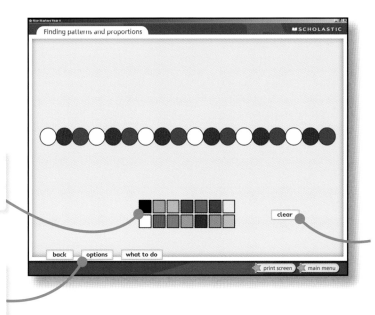

colour palette
Select different colours for pattern

'clear'
Press to clear pattern

'options'
Select number of beads required

Targets: number facts

Strand

Knowing and using number facts

Learning objective

Use knowledge of addition and subtraction facts to derive sums of numbers (up to the tenth multiple)

Type of starter

Rehearse

Whiteboard tools

● Press 'go' to generate five number cards.
● In 'options' select 'randomly generated' in order for the program to generate a target number, or select 'entered by teacher' to manually insert a number into the target.
● Use the 'notepad' to work out calculations. A 'pen' tool will automatically pop up when the notepad opens. Press 'start again' or use the 'eraser' tool to delete any text.
● Press 'winner' if children complete the activity successfully to see the winner animation.

What to do

The aim of this activity is for children to use known number facts to find a target number. Once five cards have been generated, select a target number that is achievable with the numbers shown and type it into the 'bull's eye'. In 'random mode' the target number will be generated automatically. Encourage the children to use known strategies in order to write number sentences that match (or nearly match) the target number. Invite individual children to write their calculations on the on-screen notepad and review the process. At this point, encourage the rest of the class to challenge the process or calculations used - or suggest an alternative method.

Differentiation

Less confident: at this age, children should be encouraged to use all four standard number operations (+,–, × and ÷), though you might initially limit the activity to addition and subtraction facts. For additional support, provide each child with a copy of the photocopiable 'Targets' sheet on page 44.
More confident: children should be taught and encouraged to use simple squared numbers (for example, $5^2 \times 5 = 125$). Ask: *Would the target be achieved faster using this method? Why?*

Key questions:

● *What strategies are the most efficient? How do they help you to 'hit the target'?*
● *What tips would you give somebody who was new to the game?*

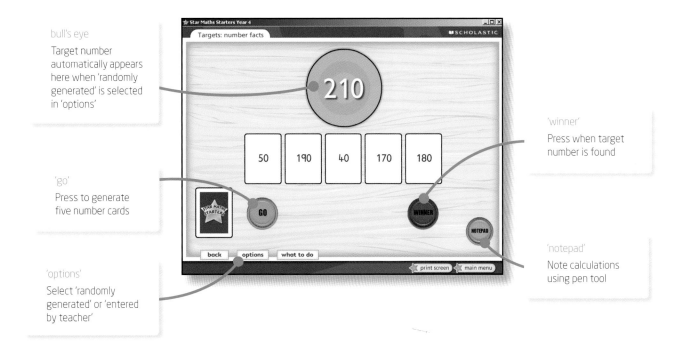

bull's eye
Target number automatically appears here when 'randomly generated' is selected in 'options'

'winner'
Press when target number is found

'go'
Press to generate five number cards

'notepad'
Note calculations using pen tool

'options'
Select 'randomly generated' or 'entered by teacher'

Place value (ITP)

Strand

Knowing and using number facts

Learning objective

Use knowledge of addition and subtraction facts and place value to derive sums and differences of pairs of multiples of 10, 100 or 1000

Type of starter

Refine

Whiteboard tools

- Press the three 'number maker' buttons to make the 100s, 10s or 1s place value cards.
- The place value cards should snap to each other and can either be partitioned or deleted. Each card also has a small arrow at the bottom left-hand corner. Pressing this arrow reveals a set of counters that represent the number, which is a useful visual aid.
- User side: this changes the side that the user has control of the main tool buttons. It is set to the right by default.

What to do

Use this ITP to refine skills in both partitioning numbers and working out differences between two numbers. To begin this activity, create two three-digit numbers from the place value buttons. Take care in placing the cards on top of one another. Once created, ask the class to partition the numbers ensuring that they are aware of how to partition and then use these partitioned numbers to demonstrate how they can work out the difference between them.

Differentiation

Less confident: ask the children to break down just one number and to read out the place value cards that make up the number. Use the counters as a visual aid.
More confident: compare two numbers. Ask: *How can we use place value units to work out differences?*

Key questions

- *What is the difference between the two numbers?*
- *How do the cards help you to understand place value?*

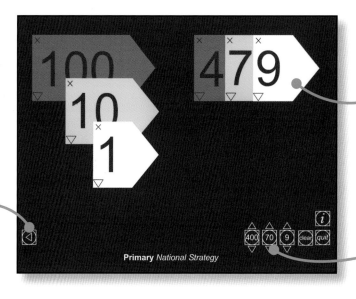

place value cards
Snap into place when placed on top of one another

user side
Changes toolbar to left

number maker
- Press up or down arrows to make numbers
- Press number to create 100s, 10s and 1s place value cards

Multiplication square

Strand

Knowing and using number facts

Learning objective

Derive and recall multiplication facts up to 10 × 10

Type of starter

Rehearse

Whiteboard tools

- Press the 'highlight' or 'clear' button and then select any square to reveal the number beneath.
- Press the 'hide' button and then select square(s) to conceal numbers.

What to do

Prepare the multiplication square before the lesson: select one number on the 10 × 10 multiplication grid and leave all the remaining numbers hidden.

Challenge the children to find all the other numbers in the multiplication square. The key to this activity is in the selection of questions as this will draw out the children's understanding of the times tables up to 10 × 10. After each selection, press the square to confirm or refute their answers. Ask for more than one answer before revealing the missing number.

Differentiation

Less confident: ask less confident learners to select numbers only after some patterns have already been established in the grid.
More confident: ask children to tell you the whole row or column once one number in that row or column has been established.

Key questions

- *Can you predict the numbers above and below the number showing?*
- *What are the numbers to the left and right of the number showing?*
- *Who can tell me the numbers in a whole row or column?*

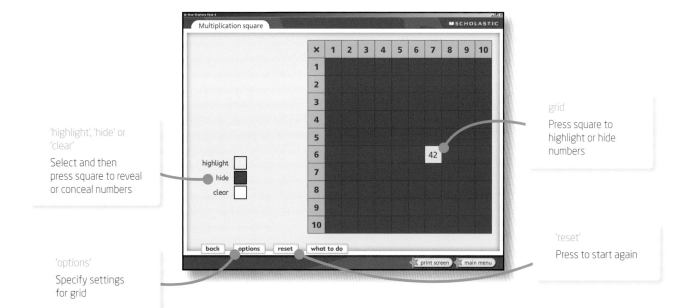

'highlight', 'hide' or 'clear'

Select and then press square to reveal or conceal numbers

'options'

Specify settings for grid

grid

Press square to highlight or hide numbers

'reset'

Press to start again

Bingo: times tables up to 10 × 10

Strand

Knowing and using number facts

Learning objective

Derive and recall multiplication facts up to 10 × 10

Type of starter

Rehearse

Whiteboard tools

- Use the 'set timer' menu to adjust time between bingo calls (5-20 seconds).
- Press the 'start' button to start a new game.
- Press 'check grid' to check answers if someone calls *House*.
- Press 'play on' or 'winner' after checking a player's grid.

What to do

This activity is designed to rehearse number facts and encourage quick recall of multiples up to 10 × 10 against a time limit. Provide each child or, alternatively, each pair with a bingo card, which can be printed from the opening screen or prepared using the bingo card template on page 45.

Each ball offers a different number sentence. If the answer appears on their bingo grid, the children mark it off. If the children are new to the game allow for a longer amount of time between bingo calls. If a child calls *House* (or other similar winning call), press 'check grid' to pause the game and call up the checking grid, which includes all of the completed number sentences that have been called. If they are correct press the 'winner' button for an appropriate fanfare or press 'play on' to continue the game.

Differentiation

Less confident: simplify the game by extending the time between questions and asking the children to call *House* after correctly identifying five answers. Allow some children to use a multiplication grid, which will enable them to both speed up their reference of numbers and product recall.

More confident: increase the number of answers on the bingo cards using the bingo card template on page 45.

Key questions

- *How can you check that your answer is correct?* (For example, tests of divisibility - ask for some examples of this.)
- *What strategies did you use to help you to recall these tables facts?*

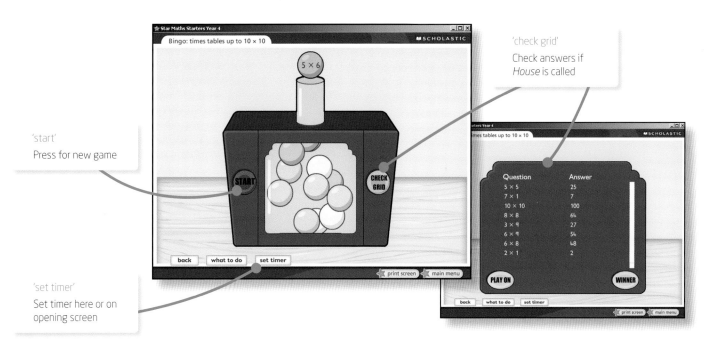

'check grid'
Check answers if *House* is called

'start'
Press for new game

'set timer'
Set timer here or on opening screen

Dominoes: multiplication

Strand

Knowing and using number facts

Learning objective

Derive and recall multiplication facts up to 10×10

Type of starter

Rehearse

Whiteboard tools

- Press 'new' to start a new game.
- Press the 'miss a go' button to take another domino from the pot.
- Domino
  - Drag and drop into the game
  - Press to rotate 90°
- Press 'winner' if Player 1 or Player 2 has placed all of the dominoes.

What to do

The aim of this game is to match the domino answers with the appropriate equations. The game is played in the same way as regular dominoes with two groups playing against each other. Each 'player' (maximum of two) is dealt five dominoes. A starter domino is selected by the computer to begin the game and the players then take turns to play. If a player is unable to place a domino they must take one from the central pot. Play continues until a player places all of their dominoes, and is declared the winner, or there are no dominoes left in the pot. If a stalemate situation is created, in which neither player can play a domino and the pot is empty, the player with fewest remaining dominoes is the winner.

Differentiation

Less confident: use 'talk partners' to discuss moves, which will help to support a child's confidence and affirm their decisions.
More confident: play 'beat the teacher', in which children pit themselves against an adult in the classroom. Ask children to look for two multiplication sentences with the same product (for example, 4×4 and 2×8).

Key questions

- *How can we identify which dominoes to use?*
- *What strategies would you use in order to block your opponent?*

domino
- Drag domino to playing space
- Press domino to rotate it

'new'
Press to start new game

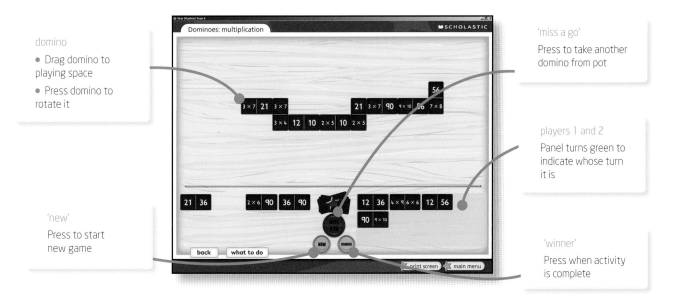

'miss a go'
Press to take another domino from pot

players 1 and 2
Panel turns green to indicate whose turn it is

'winner'
Press when activity is complete

Number dials (ITP)

Strand

Knowing and using number facts

Learning objective

Derive and recall multiplication facts up to 10 × 10, the corresponding division facts and multiples of numbers to 10 up to the tenth multiple

Type of starter

Refine

Whiteboard tools

- Press the outside box numbers once to reveal and again to hide.
- Press the small 'clock' face button at the bottom right of the screen to reveal numbers on the main 'clock' face. Each number can be individually hidden or revealed by pressing it.
- The focus number in the centre of the clock is the key factor. This can be changed or hidden by pressing the number square at the bottom of the screen.
- Use the 'dice' button to create random numbers. The multi-dice randomly change the clock numbers, while the single dice changes the focus number in the centre.

What to do

The aim of this activity is to refine multiplication skills by identifying the hidden numbers on the number dial. On starting the program, the central factor number (that has a range of 2–10) is revealed, with the respective numbers from 1–10 surrounding it. Options on the screen allow the user to change either the central factor or the location of the clock numbers (they can also be hidden). By hiding the clock numbers, the focus of the activity changes from multiplication to division.

Differentiation

Less confident: reveal the centre number and clock face numbers.
More confident: hide all the numbers and reveal pairs at a time in order to guess the central factor.

Key questions:

- *How could you write these numbers in a number sentence?*
- *How many numbers do you need to reveal before you know the centre number?*

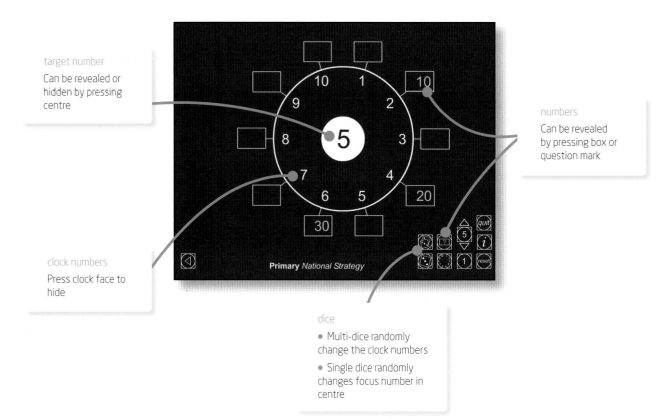

target number
Can be revealed or hidden by pressing centre

numbers
Can be revealed by pressing box or question mark

clock numbers
Press clock face to hide

dice
- Multi-dice randomly change the clock numbers
- Single dice randomly changes focus number in centre

Dominoes: fractions that total 1

Strand

Knowing and using number facts

Learning objective

Identify pairs of fractions that total 1

Type of starter

Reason

Whiteboard tools

● Press 'new' to start a new game.
● Press 'miss a go' to take another domino from the pot.
● Drag and drop the dominoes into the playing space. Press a domino to rotate it.
● Press 'winner' if Player 1 or Player 2 has placed all of the dominoes, and it is agreed that the last domino was placed correctly.

What to do

The aim of this game is to identify corresponding fraction dominoes that total 1. For example, if a domino with $3/4$ is placed on the board, a player needs to play a domino with $1/4$ (or an equivalent fraction such as $2/8$) alongside it. The game is played in the same way as regular dominoes with two groups playing against each other. Each group or 'player' (maximum of two) is dealt five dominoes.

A starter domino is selected by the computer to begin the game and the players then take turns to play. If a player is unable to place a domino they must take one from the central pot. Play continues until a player places all of their dominoes, and is declared the winner, or there are no dominoes left in the pot. If a stalemate situation is created, in which neither player can play a domino and the pot is empty, the player with fewest remaining dominoes is the winner.

Differentiation

Less confident: use 'talk partners' to help the children to find equivalent fractions for halves, quarters and eighths.
More confident: play 'beat the teacher', in which children pit themselves against an adult in the classroom.

Key questions

● *What methods did you use to identify which dominoes to select?*
● *What strategies would you use in order to block your opponent?*

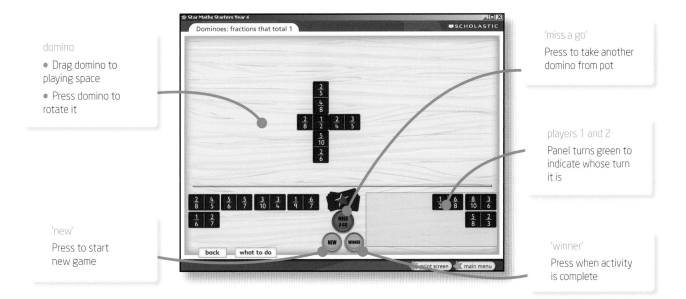

domino
● Drag domino to playing space
● Press domino to rotate it

'new'
Press to start new game

'miss a go'
Press to take another domino from pot

players 1 and 2
Panel turns green to indicate whose turn it is

'winner'
Press when activity is complete

Fractions (ITP)

Strand

Knowing and using number facts

Learning objective

Identify pairs of fractions that total 1

Type of starter

Refresh

Whiteboard tools

- Press the small green and yellow bar to produce fraction bars, up to a maximum of five.
- Press the arrows next to the fraction bar to increase or decrease the denominator, in steps of one, and show the fraction chosen.
- Press 'fdpr' to reveal the fractions, decimals, percentages and ratio equivalent to each bar.
- Press the individual fractions on each 'fractions bar' to change the colours from green to yellow to create different fractions on screen.
- Press 'reset' to clear all but the lowest green bar.

What to do

The aim of this starter is to identify corresponding fractions in order to create a whole number. Start with four bars on the screen partitioned into $\frac{1}{2}$ $\frac{1}{4}$ $\frac{1}{8}$ and $\frac{1}{16}$. Change one section of each to yellow and ask the class what the corresponding fraction would be in order to make a whole (for example, $\frac{3}{4}$ would need to be highlighted to complete the quarter bar). Next ask: *How could we make each bar equivalent to $\frac{1}{2}$? How can this be demonstrated?* Use the 'fdpr' button, selecting the D (decimals), to show that when the appropriate sections are highlighted yellow, each bar has the same decimal (in this case 0.5). Reset the bars and select a new target. It might be useful to show a fraction that cannot have the same equivalence. Ask: *How close is its decimal representation to the equivalent fraction?*

Differentiation

Less confident: review common fractions and use the bars to demonstrate equivalence.
More confident: translate the fractions to percentages in order to make 100%.

Key questions

- *How do the bars help you to 'see' the fractions?*
- *Who can identify an equivalent fraction?* (Ask individual children to come to the board to demonstrate.)

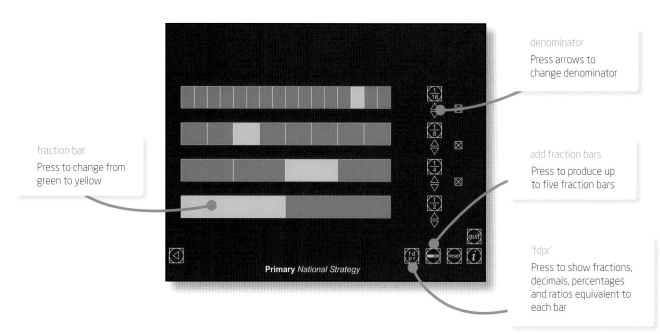

denominator
Press arrows to change denominator

fraction bar
Press to change from green to yellow

add fraction bars
Press to produce up to five fraction bars

Primary *National Strategy*

'fdpr'
Press to show fractions, decimals, percentages and ratios equivalent to each bar

Maths Boggle: addition and subtraction

Strand

Calculating

Learning objective

Add or subtract mentally pairs of two-digit whole numbers

Type of starter

Refine

Whiteboard tools
● Press 'new' to rattle the Boggle dice
● Change the target question by selecting a new question from the 'options' menu.
● Highlight each dice by pressing it once (to remove the highlight, press again).
● Press 'new' for a new set of numbers.
● Use the 'notepad' to show workings out.

What to do

The aim of this activity is to use mental methods and, where this is well established, to begin to use more sophisticated strategies to add and subtract pairs of two-digit numbers in a grid.

The game begins by selecting a question from the 'options' box (or, should you wish, by preparing your own question). Once this has been understood, the dice are 'rattled' to reveal a random selection of numbers. In pairs or individually, the children set out to find the answer by using the numbers on the screen. Once this has been achieved the teacher can highlight dice by pressing on their faces. Also, challenge the children to come to the board to show their calculations using the on-screen notepad.

Differentiation

Less confident: identify pairs of numbers that children think have the largest difference. Round the numbers to the nearest 10 and estimate before working out the difference.
More confident: extend the activity by challenging the children to add number strings (rows or columns).

Key questions
● *Add any pair of numbers. How did you work out the answer?*
● *What methods might you use to estimate or check answers?*

'new'
Press to rattle dice

'options'
Select question from menu

dice
Press to highlight

'notepad'
Press to write calculations

Function machine

Learning objective

Add or subtract mentally pairs of two-digit whole numbers

Type of starter

Reason

Whiteboard tools
- Use the 'options' menu to set the 'machine mode'. Select from 'manual' or 'random' options.
- Select 'manual' to prepare your own number sentences, or 'random' to produce a computer-generated number sentence.
- A keypad pops up automatically when you press on a window to enter a number.
- Press the 'history' button to view a list of the number sentences completed during the lesson.

What to do
The aim of this activity is to find missing two-digit numbers or the function in order to complete a number sentence. Either the teacher or the computer can generate these using either the 'random' or 'manual' mode options.

Manual mode: enter some number sentences involving the addition or subtraction of pairs of two-digit numbers, for example, 21 + 19, 33 - 21. Use the drop-down menu in the function window to select either a + or - operation. Press 'go' to check answers.

Random mode: the computer selects a number sentence, but hides the input, output and function windows on the machine. Decide which element to reveal first and press that window to open it. After one other element has been revealed, ask the children to write down and then display the missing number or function. Check their answers and then press 'go' to check the answer on the machine.

Differentiation
Less confident: work in 'manual' mode and limit the number range as required.
More confident: sequences can be demonstrated using the machine. For example, adding 20 to a number can be modelled by keeping the function to +20 and keying the created output number back into the input, thereby adding 20 to the number each time. A record of this will be kept in the 'history' box.

Key questions
- *How did you work out the missing part of the sentence?*
- *How much of the sentence needs to be revealed before you can complete it?*

'new'
- Press to begin new number sentence in 'manual' mode
- Press for number sentence in 'random' mode

'options'
- Select 'manual' mode to enter your own numbers
- Select 'random' mode for computer-generated numbers, initially hidden

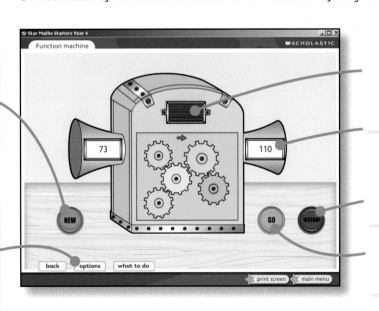

windows
- Type numbers and functions in 'manual' mode
- Press to open in 'random' mode

'history'
Press to view record of completed number sentences

'go'
Press to check answer

Shopping

Strand

Calculating

Learning objective

Refine and use efficient written methods to add £.p

Type of starter

Refine

Whiteboard tools

- Drag two items from the shop into the shopping basket.
- Press 'check-out' to take the basket to the till on the next screen.
- Drag the appropriate amount of money into the till to make the exact total to pay.
- Press the 'sale' button to check if the amount paid is correct.
- Press 'clear' to empty the till and try again to pay the exact amount of money.
- Press 'back to shop' to return to the first screen and to start a new sale.

What to do

This activity is designed to refine standard written methods to add two sums of money with adjustment from pounds to pence. Ask the children to select two items in the on-screen shop and drag them into the shopping basket. Press the 'check-out' button to move on to the next screen. Challenge the children to work out the total using individual whiteboards and discuss the calculations in class. Finally, ask them to work out the notes and coins you would use to pay for the items and move them into the on-screen till. Press 'sale' to check calculations and the exact total.

Differentiation

Less confident: select items that will produce smaller totals (for example, £3.50 or less) in order to build confidence. Allow longer for pairs or individual children to work out each total using written methods.

More confident: ask children to round the cost of each item and estimate the total before proceeding with the exact calculation.

Key questions

- *What is the total cost of both items?*
- *What coins could you use to pay for both items?*

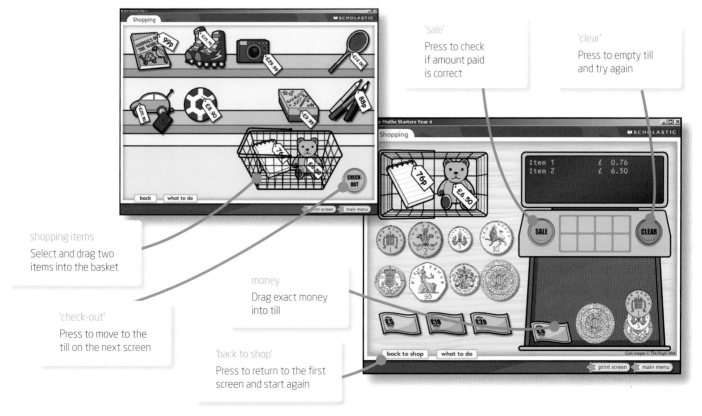

'sale'
Press to check if amount paid is correct

'clear'
Press to empty till and try again

shopping items
Select and drag two items into the basket

money
Drag exact money into till

'check-out'
Press to move to the till on the next screen

'back to shop'
Press to return to the first screen and start again

Bingo: times tables (×10 and ×100)

Strand

Calculating

Learning objective

Multiply numbers to 1000 by 10 and then 100 (whole-number answers)

Type of starter

Refine

Whiteboard tools
● Use the 'set timer' menu to adjust time between bingo calls (5-20 seconds).
● Press the 'start' button to start a new game.
● Press 'check grid' to check answers if someone calls *House*.
● Press 'play on' or 'winner' after checking a player's grid.

What to do

This activity is designed to rehearse number facts and encourage quick recall of multiples of 10 and 100 against a time limit. Provide each child or, alternatively, each pair with a bingo card, which can be printed from the opening screen or prepared using the bingo card template on page 45.

Each ball offers a different number sentence. If the answer appears on the children's bingo grid, ask them to mark it off. If the children are new to the game, allow for a longer amount of time between bingo calls. If a child calls *House* (or other similar winning call), press the 'check grid' button to pause the game and call up the completed number sentences that have been called. If they are correct, press the 'winner' button for an appropriate fanfare or press 'play on' to continue the game.

Differentiation

Less confident: simplify the game by extending the time between questions and asking the children to call *House* after correctly identifying five answers.
More confident: increase the number of answers on the bingo cards using the bingo card template on page 45. Challenge the children to make division sentences from the multiplication sentences they have identified.

Key questions

● *You know that 44 × 100 = 4400. What division sentence can you make from this?*
● *Where would you come across numbers that are multiplied by 10 or 100?* (Ask the children to consider how the metric system works and that numbers can be illustrated either as decimal or multiples of 100. For example, 23cm is equal to 230mm or 3 litres are equal to 3000ml.)

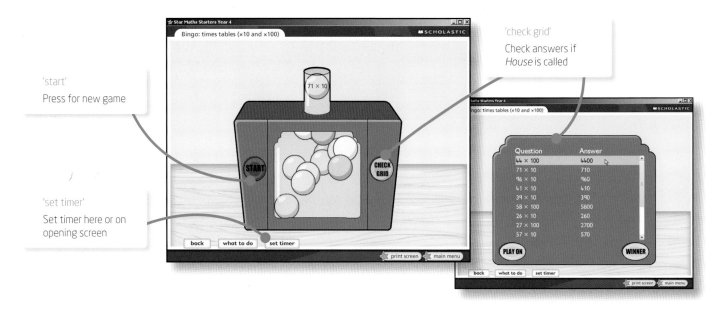

'start'
Press for new game

'set timer'
Set timer here or on opening screen

'check grid'
Check answers if *House* is called

Finding reflections

Strand

Understanding shape

Learning objective

Draw polygons and identify their properties, including their line symmetry

Type of starter

Refine

Whiteboard tools

- Use the 'options' menu to select the direction of the mirror line (horizontal, vertical or diagonal), and to specify the size of the grid.
- Draw a shape in the white area. When complete, press 'done'.
- Draw the reflection in the new white area. When complete, press 'done'.
- Press on a white or coloured square if you wish to change either the object or the image.
- Press 'check' to see if the reflection drawn is correct.
- Press 'reset' to clear the grid and start again.

What to do

Use this activity to help children understand the need for an image to be equidistant from the object in relation to the mirror line. Make the object or shape as simple or complex as you and your children wish to build it. Ask children to come to the board to build the object and, of course, to draw the reflected image.

Differentiation

Less confident: start with simple objects only one square away from the mirror line.
More confident: draw more complex shapes two or three squares away from the mirror line. The program also includes options for diagonal and horizontal mirror lines if you wish to extend the activity further.

Key questions

- *How many blank squares are there between each small square and the mirror line?*
- *Where would the image of this object be after reflection?*

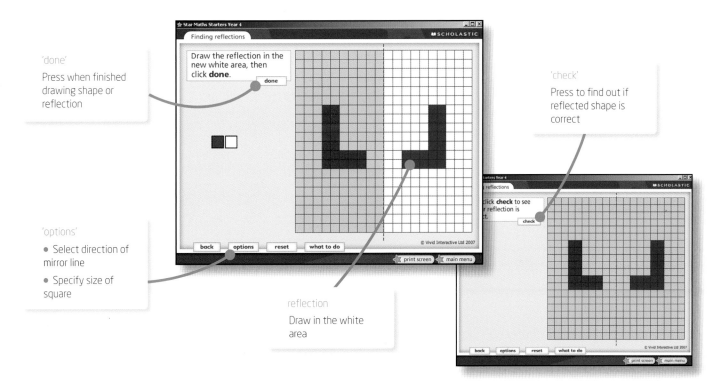

'done'
Press when finished drawing shape or reflection

'options'
- Select direction of mirror line
- Specify size of square

reflection
Draw in the white area

'check'
Press to find out if reflected shape is correct

Maps and directions

Strand

Understanding shape

Learning objective

Use the eight compass points to describe direction

Type of starter

Rehearse

Whiteboard tools

- Press the 'new' button to generate a map with some paths blocked by roadworks, and three objects to collect.
- Drag and drop the direction cards to prepare the route. Select one 'direction' card and one 'movement' card each time. NOTE: the order of these cards makes a difference to turning first or moving first.
- Press 'move' to confirm the selection and move the recycling lorry along the route.
- Press the 'show route' button to display the directions selected so far.
- View the box at the top of the screen to identify which items the lorry has collected along the route.

What to do

This activity develops children's use of all eight compass points. From a given starting point ask the children for directions to guide the lorry to the recycling centre using the direction cards on the screen as prompts. Drag and drop each card into place to build up the route. More than one route is available and the routes include barriers and objects to collect, so the quickest route is not necessarily the best. At any time during the activity, you can press the 'show route' button to check the lorry's progress. Encourage the children to check and challenge the route at this stage and start again if necessary. Press 'move' when the route is confirmed. The lorry will then make its way round the screen - hopefully always finishing at the recycling centre to deposit its contents! Make sure at all times children use the correct mathematical vocabulary when selecting an instruction from the screen.

Differentiation

Less confident: give the children copies of the photocopiable 'Maps and directions' sheet on page 46 as additional support.
More confident: ask children for alternative ways of giving the same directions (for example, rotating through 90° clockwise).

Key questions

- *What is the most direct way to move from this point to that?*
- *Are there any alternative ways of moving from this point to that?*

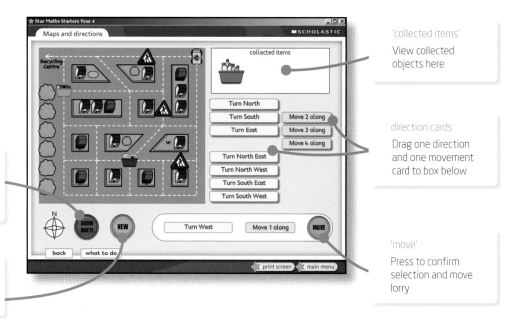

'collected items'
View collected objects here

direction cards
Drag one direction and one movement card to box below

'show route'
Press to see directions selected so far

'new'
Press to generate a new map

'move'
Press to confirm selection and move lorry

Find the alien: coordinates

Strand

Understanding shape

Learning objective

Describe and identify the position of a point on a grid of squares

Type of starter

Reason

Whiteboard tools

● Type in the horizontal coordinate and then the vertical coordinate to select a point.
● A keypad pops up automatically when you press on the white boxes to enter a number.
● Press 'check' to confirm the choice.
● Press 'new' to start a new game with the alien in a different position.

What to do

The aim of the activity is to find a point on a 5 × 5 grid in which an alien is hiding. Tell the children that they should use coordinates to identify each point. The position of the alien is randomly selected each time. After each selection, a square will be revealed. To narrow the selections down and prevent the activity becoming a guessing game, one of three messages appears after each selection: 'vertical is correct' or 'horizontal is correct' as appropriate, or – if neither the row nor the column is correct – 'have another go!' appears. When the alien spacecraft has been found, the space scene is completed and an alien noise is sounded! Children should respond positively to this activity and will start to develop logical processes through the careful selection of points to find the alien in the fewest selections.

Differentiation

Less confident: ask children for coordinates early in the activity while the choice of square is still quite random to ensure that they understand the horizontal and vertical numbering system.
More confident: ask children about possible strategies to find the alien in the smallest number of goes.

Key questions

● *How can you describe, for example, the point in the top-left hand corner using horizontal and vertical coordinates?*
● *Which possible point could the alien be in, now we know the horizontal or vertical gridline he is hiding on?*

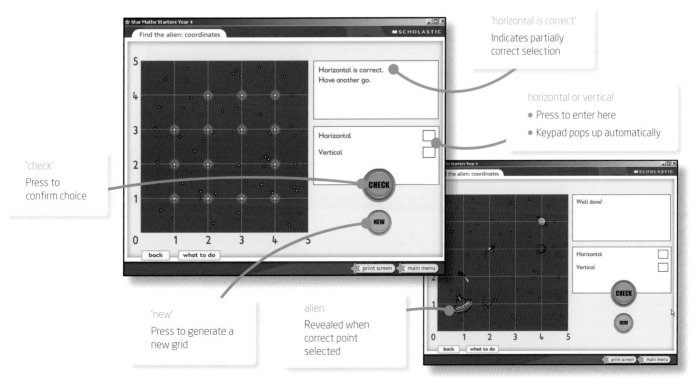

'horizontal is correct'
Indicates partially correct selection

horizontal or vertical
● Press to enter here
● Keypad pops up automatically

'check'
Press to confirm choice

'new'
Press to generate a new grid

alien
Revealed when correct point selected

Calculating angles (ITP)

Strand

Understanding shape

Learning objective

Know that angles are measured in degrees and that one turn is 360°; compare and order angles less than 180°

Type of starter

Reason

Whiteboard tools

● Press the angle menu button and select the 180° angle.
● Press the 'shape' button and select a shape from the menu. This will appear on the 180° angle, creating two unmarked angles.
● Press the question marks to reveal the angles.
● Change the colour of shapes added by pressing the green square and selecting a different colour from the menu.

What to do

Remind the children there are 180° in a straight line. Press the angle menu button and add a 180° angle to the screen. Next, select a shape from the 'shape' menu. This will appear on the 180° angle, creating two unmarked angles. The angles will automatically appear as question marks. Press one to reveal the angle and ask the children to work out what the other angle will be.

Differentiation

Less confident: consolidate measuring an angle round a point using just a single shape on a 90° base.
More confident: begin measuring and estimating angles that are between 180° and 360°. Ask: *How could we estimate the size of angle round a point with these shapes?*

Key questions

● *When multiples of a regular shape are used (for example, an equilateral triangle), what happens to the outside angle? Is there a pattern?*
● *Are there any shapes where we already know their angles? If so, what are they?*

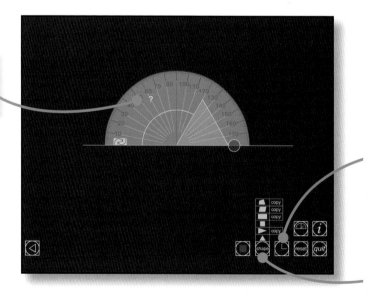

angles
Press question mark to reveal angle

angle menu
Select 180° angle from menu

'shape'
Select shape to add to 180° angle

Maths Boggle: measurements

Strand

Measuring

Learning objective

Choose and use standard metric units and their abbreviations when estimating, measuring and recording and, where appropriate, use decimal notation to record measurements

Type of starter

Refine

Whiteboard tools
- Press 'new' to rattle the Boggle dice.
- Change the target by selecting a new question from the 'options' menu.
- Highlight each dice by pressing it once (to remove the highlight, press again).
- Press 'new' for a new set of numbers.
- Use the 'notepad' to show calculations.

What to do
The aim of this activity is to use mental methods to add a number of measurements together, and then to convert the measurements from centimetres to metres using decimal notation.

Start the game by selecting a target question from the 'options' menu (or, should you wish, by stating your own target). Once this has been understood, the dice are 'rattled' to reveal a random selection of measurements in a grid. In pairs or individually, the children set out to find the answer by using these numbers. The teacher can then highlight dice by pressing them. Challenge children to come to the board to show their workings out using the on-screen notepad.

Differentiation
Less confident: focus the children on converting centimetres to metres and recording using decimal notation.
More confident: in mixed-ability groups, ask more confident children to take responsibility for adding the strings of measurements.

Key questions
- *How do doubles speed up the adding process?*
- *What methods might you use to check answers?* (For example, finding doubles or multiples of a number, adding near doubles, identifying number bonds.)

dice
Press to highlight

'new'
Press to rattle dice

'options'
Select questions from menu

target question
Select from 'options' menu at foot of screen

'notepad'
Use the pen tool to show calculations

Weighing scales

Strand

Measuring

Learning objective

Know the meaning of 'kilo' and, where appropriate, use decimal notation to record measurements

Type of starter

Read

Whiteboard tools
● Drag and drop items on the left of the screen into the pan or add some preset weights.
● Remove items from the pan by dragging them off.
● Turn the digital readout off or on.
● Select 'options' to make changes to the divisions on the face of the scales.

What to do
The aim of this activity is to accurately read and measure weights in kilograms and grams. Drag a number of items onto the scales' pan. Ask the children to write the weight in kilos (using decimal notation) on their individual whiteboards and then to show their partners. Use the digital readout to check the children's answers. Assess any misconceptions or errors and ask the children to explain how the face of the scales can help when reading the weight.

Repeat the activity over a number of sessions to check how quickly and confidently the children are able to read the measurements on the scales.

Differentiation
Less confident: use the 'options' menu to increase the subdivisions on the scales' face to 10.
More confident: ask the children to show their answers in grams as well as kilograms (for example, 2360g = 2.36kg) and to estimate to the nearest ten grams.

Key questions
● What is the total weight of these two items?
● What do the divisions on the scales represent? How would we be able to estimate the weight of each object?

products
Drag food items or preset weights onto the scales

'options'
Set maximum weight, subdivision, and whether or not to show numbers on analogue scale

scales' pan
Add or remove items by dragging them on or off

digital readout
Can be turned on or off, on analogue scales, to reveal exact weight of items

Measuring jug

Strand

Measuring

Learning objective

Interpret intervals and divisions on partially numbered scales and record readings accurately

Type of starter

Refine

Whiteboard tools

- Press the 'options' button to set the following: set 'scale' to 1000ml; set subdivisions to 2 (to give 50ml intervals on the jug); and set 'fill steps' to manual.
- Press 'in' to fill the jug, and press it again to stop filling.
- Press 'out' to empty the jug, and press it again to stop emptying.
- Press 'reset' to start again.

What to do

Ask the children to read aloud together the marked divisions on the measuring jug. Next, question individual children about the unmarked divisions and ask them to read these aloud. Fill the jug part way up to a certain level (for example, 300ml) and then question them about the reading. Fill and empty the jug to find the difference between the two levels. Set some problems of the type below (see 'Key questions') and ask the children to write the answers on their individual whiteboards. Check the answers using the measuring jug.

Differentiation

Less confident: in the early stages ask children to read the scale to the nearest 50ml mark.
More confident: challenge the children by asking if they can suggest a more accurate reading.

Key questions

- *A carton of orange holds 200ml. How many cartons could be taken from the full jug?*
- *A baby's bottle holds 250ml. If she only drinks 100ml, how much is left over?*

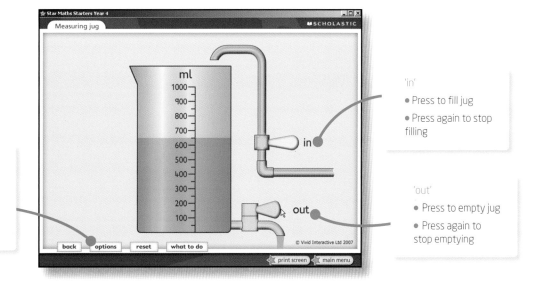

Finding area and perimeter

Strand

Measuring

Learning objective

Draw rectangles and measure and calculate their perimeters; find the area of rectilinear shapes drawn on a square grid by counting squares

Type of starter

Refine

Whiteboard tools
● Use the 'options' menu to specify the size of the grid.
● Use the highlighters to build up shapes on the grid.
● Press on a white or coloured square if you wish to change the shape.
● Press 'clear' to start again.

What to do

Use this tool to build up rectangles and other shapes with small coloured squares. Build different shapes with the children's input - for example a rectangle made up of 12 squares - and investigate the areas and perimeters of the shapes formed. In this example, assume that each small square is 1 cm × 1 cm so that perimeter is measured in cm and area in cm². Also, challenge children to draw rectangles with a specific area (for example, 28 cm²), then ask the class: *Is there more than one way of doing this?*

Differentiation

Less confident: start with simple rectangles until children get used to the concepts of area and perimeter and to the process of counting squares and lengths.
More confident: encourage children to investigate the areas of different rectangles and ask if they can identify a method of finding the areas without counting squares.

Key questions

● *How many small squares are used in the shapes drawn?*
● *If you trace all round the outside of the shape and add up all the lengths, how long is this altogether?*
● *Draw two shapes on the grid and ask: Which shape has the largest area? How do you know?*

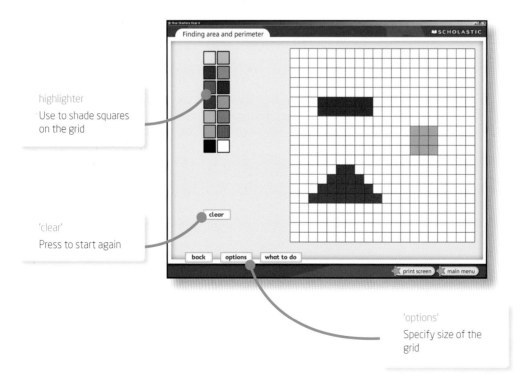

highlighter
Use to shade squares on the grid

'clear'
Press to start again

'options'
Specify size of the grid

Clocks: time differences

Strand

Measuring

Learning objective

Read time to the nearest minute; calculate time intervals from clocks

Type of starter

Read

Whiteboard tools

- Press the 'randomise' button to select a random digital or analogue time on the clocks.
- Drag the clock hands manually to move the time on the analogue clock; set the hour and minutes on the digital clock by pressing the + and – signs.
- Use the 'options' button to specify the settings for the 'randomise' functions. You can also choose to link the hour and minutes hands on the analogue clock.
- Set the digital clock to '12 hour' mode.

What to do

The aim of this activity is to work out, in hours and minutes, the difference between the two clocks. Start by pressing the 'randomise' button under the analogue clock and ask the class to call out the time. Repeat three or four times to assess that the children are able to read the time to the nearest minute with confidence. Next, press the 'randomise' button on both the analogue and digital clocks and ask the children to work out the time difference between the two. To adapt the game you might either change both or just one clock face.

Differentiation

Less confident: if children find it challenging to read minute divisions on the clock, adjust the time by dragging the minute hand to the nearest whole five-minute interval (the hour hand will adjust accordingly if you select 'link hands' in 'options').
More confident: ask the children to assume that the analogue clock represents a.m. and the digital clock represents p.m. Can they tell you what the time difference would be?

Key questions:

- *How can we make rough estimates between the times?*
- *What is the difference between a.m. and p.m.* (a.m. antemeridian, p.m. post meridian), *and why does it matter?*

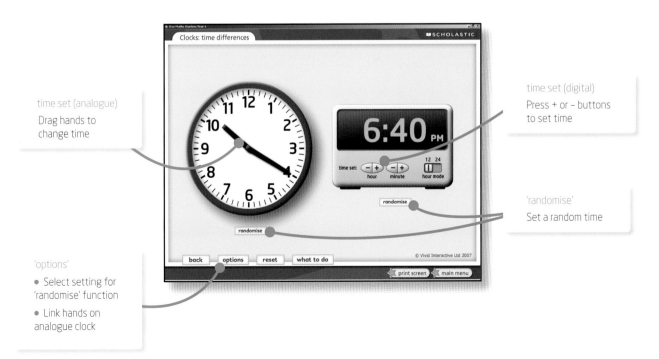

time set (analogue)
Drag hands to change time

time set (digital)
Press + or – buttons to set time

'randomise'
Set a random time

'options'
- Select setting for 'randomise' function
- Link hands on analogue clock

Favourite colours

Strand

Handling data

Learning objective

Present, analyse and interpret data in bar charts using ICT

Type of starter

Refine

Whiteboard tools
● Using a keyboard, type the title of the chart and label the axes in the data table.
● Press an empty column segment to fill it.
● Press a column segment to remove a bar.
● Press the 'options' button to extend or change the scale of the bar chart.

What to do
Find out the children's favourite colours by a show of hands or asking round the class. When the data has been collected, record it by entering the label information into the bar chart using a keyboard and pressing columns of the grid to increase or decrease the length of each bar. Print off the resulting bar chart. If the y scale is greater than 10 then use the options buttons to enable you to extend this. Repeat this activity using other data from the class on other occasions. Ask a number of questions relating to each bar chart. For example: *What is the favourite colour? By how many? What was the least favourite? What is the difference between the favourite and least favourite?*

Differentiation
Less confident: ask children to come to the front of the class and press the appropriate box to select their favourite colour.
More confident: try adjusting the y scale and discuss with the children how many blocks they would need to add each time.

Key questions
● *Why is it much easier to see the favourite colours of the class in a bar chart rather than just using a list?*
● *Would the bar chart look any different if it went up in steps of 2 or 5 rather than in steps of 1?*

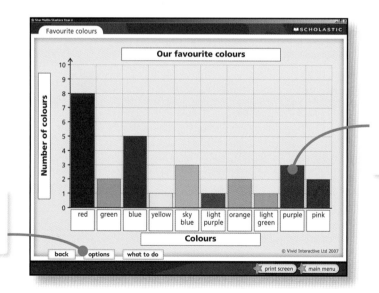

options
Press to alter scale of bar chart

grid
Press individual columns to increase or decrease their length

Pirates: number line

1300
1200
1100
1000
900
800
700
600
500
400
300
200
100
0

Targets

■ Find the target numbers using the cards below.

■ How I worked out the target answer.

_____

_____

_____

_____

_____

_____

_____

_____

Bingo cards

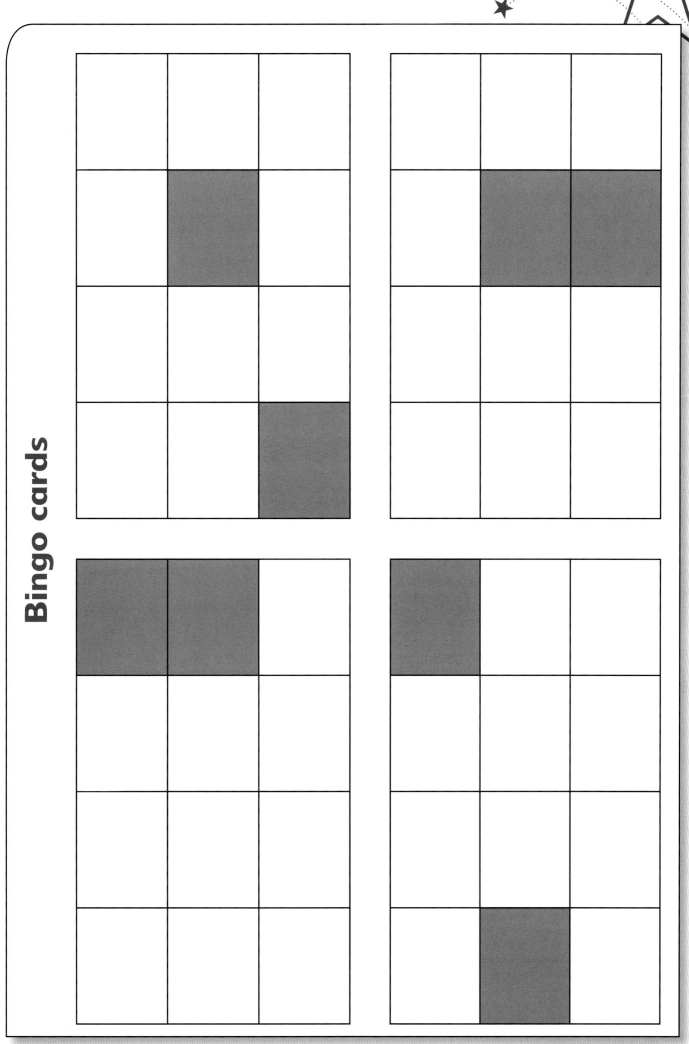

Maps and directions

▪ Plan your route using the map below.

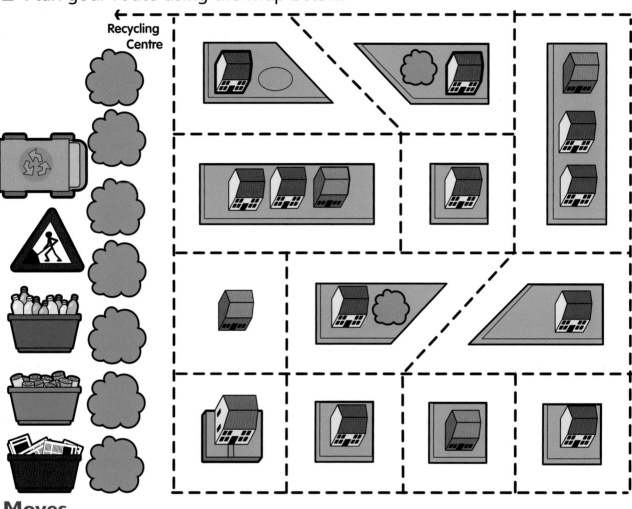

Recycling
Centre

Moves

_____

_____

_____

_____

_____

_____

_____

Teacher's name _____

Star Maths Starters diary page

Name of Star Starter	PNS objectives covered	How was activity used	Date activity was used

Also available in this series:

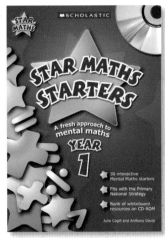
ISBN 978-1407-10007-4

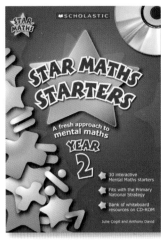
ISBN 978-1407-10008-1

ISBN 978-1407-10009-8

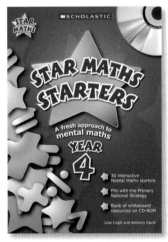
ISBN 978-1407-10010-4

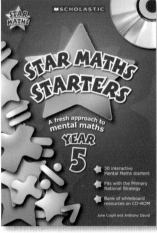
ISBN 978-1407-10011-1

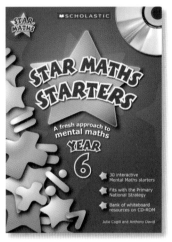
ISBN 978-1407-10012-8

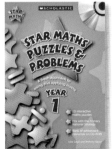
ISBN 978-1407-10031-9

ISBN 978-1407-10032-6

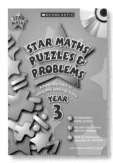
ISBN 978-1407-10033-3

ISBN 978-1407-10034-0

ISBN 978-1407-10035-7

ISBN 978-1407-10036-4

To find out more, call: 0845 603 9091
or visit our website www.scholastic.co.uk